Peanuts for Everybody

Selected Cartoons from WE'RE RIGHT
BEHIND YOU, CHARLIE BROWN, Vol. 1

Charles M. Schulz

CORONET BOOKS
Hodder Fawcett, London

Copyright © 1958, 1959, 1960, 1961, 1962, 1963, 1964 by
United Feature Syndicate Inc.

First published by Fawcett Publications Inc., New York

Coronet edition 1970
Ninth impression 1977

Printed in Great Britain for
Hodder Fawcett Ltd.,
Mill Road, Dunton Green, Sevenoaks, Kent
(Editorial Office, 47 Bedford Square,
London, WC1 3DP) by
C. Nicholls & Company Ltd.
The Philips Park Press, Manchester

ISBN 0 340 12609 4

WELL, THAT ENDED THE GAME, SNOOPY! YOU AND I ARE GETTING TO BE A GREAT DOUBLE-PLAY COMBINATION...WE REALLY WORK TOGETHER...

BY THE WAY, WOULD YOU LIKE TO COME OVER TO MY HOUSE? I'VE ASKED CHARLIE BROWN, AND FRIEDA AND VIOLET, AND I THOUGHT WE COULD...

OFF THE FIELD I MAKE MY OWN FRIENDS!

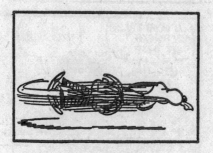

DON'T BE DISCOURAGED, CHARLIE BROWN...A TREE HOUSE IS NOT THE EASIEST THING IN THE WORLD TO BUILD...

PTUI!

PTUI!

UNTIL IT IS DEMONSTRATED, ONE FORGETS THE REALLY GREAT DIFFERENCE THAT EXISTS BETWEEN THE MERELY COMPETENT AMATEUR AND THE VERY EXPERT PROFESSIONAL!

I THINK WE HAD BETTER TRY TO PINPOINT YOUR FEARS...IF WE CAN FIND OUT WHAT IT IS YOU'RE AFRAID OF, WE CAN LABEL IT...

ARE YOU AFRAID OF RESPONSIBILITY? IF YOU ARE, THEN YOU HAVE HYPENGYOPHOBIA!

I DON'T THINK THAT'S QUITE IT..

HOW ABOUT CATS? IF YOU'RE AFRAID OF CATS, YOU HAVE AILUROPHOBIA

WELL, SORT OF.. BUT I'M NOT SURE...

ARE YOU AFRAID OF STAIRCASES? IF YOU ARE, THEN YOU HAVE CLIMACOPHOBIA

MAYBE YOU HAVE THALASSOPHOBIA..THIS IS A FEAR OF THE OCEAN, OR GEPHYROPHOBIA, WHICH IS A FEAR OF CROSSING BRIDGES...

OR MAYBE YOU HAVE PANTOPHOBIA.. DO YOU THINK YOU MIGHT HAVE PANTOPHOBIA?

WHAT'S PANTOPHOBIA?

THE FEAR OF EVERYTHING..

THAT'S IT!!!

IT'S KIND OF COLD TONIGHT...IT SHOULDN'T BE SO COLD THIS TIME OF YEAR...

I WONDER IF SNOOPY IS WARM ENOUGH...

I THINK I'LL TAKE MY SLEEPING BAG OUT TO HIM..

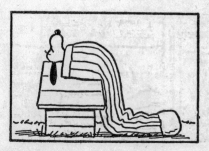

WELL, I DID IT! I'VE COLLECTED OVER A DOZEN DIFFERENT KINDS OF LEAVES!

MY ONLY PROBLEM CAME IN SELECTING WHAT SORT OF BOOK I SHOULD PRESS THEM IN..OF COURSE, I KNEW IT HAD TO BE A LARGE VOLUME...

I FIRST THOUGHT OF "THE DECLINE AND FALL OF THE ROMAN EMPIRE," AND THEN I CONSIDERED "LOOK HOMEWARD ANGEL," BUT I FINALLY DECIDED ON A VOLUME CALLED, "THE PROPHECIES OF DANIEL" BECAUSE I FELT THAT..

GET OUT OF HERE!

PEOPLE REALLY AREN'T INTERESTED IN HEARING YOU TALK ABOUT YOUR HOBBY..

YOU NEVER KNOW IN WHICH PART OF THE COUNTRY IT WILL HAPPEN..

ON HALLOWEEN NIGHT IN 1959 THE GREAT PUMPKIN APPEARED IN THE PUMPKIN PATCH OF BOOTS RUTMAN OF CONNECTICUT..

IF YOU DON'T BELIEVE ME, LOOK IN THE RECORD!

IN 1960 THE GREAT PUMPKIN APPEARED IN THE PUMPKIN PATCH OF R.W. DANIELS OF TEXAS...

AGAIN I SAY, IF YOU DON'T BELIEVE ME, LOOK IN THE RECORD!

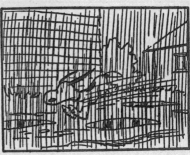

IT SNOWED LAST NIGHT..I CAN TELL!

HOW DISGUSTING! I GO TO SLEEP AT NIGHT, AND WHEN I WAKE UP, WINTER HAS COME!

SEE? THIS IS A DUPLICATE OF A SCROLL OF ISAIAH...CHAPTERS 38 TO 40...IT WAS MADE FROM SEVENTEEN PIECES OF SHEEPSKIN, AND WAS FOUND IN A CAVE BY A SHEPHERD...

HERE I'VE MADE A COPY OF THE EARLIEST KNOWN FRAGMENT EVER FOUND...IT'S A PORTION OF I SAMUEL 23: 9-16...I'LL TRY TO EXPLAIN TO THE CLASS HOW THESE MANUSCRIPTS HAVE INFLUENCED MODERN SCHOLARS...

VERY INTERESTING..

I THOUGHT IT MIGHT BE AT LEAST FAINTLY APPROPRIATE TO THE SEASON..

ARE YOU BRINGING SOMETHING FOR "SHOW AND TELL", CHARLIE BROWN?

WELL, I HAD A LITTLE RED FIRE ENGINE HERE, BUT I THINK MAYBE I'LL JUST FORGET IT..

OH, NO! DON'T TELL ME! NOT AGAIN!

HERE'S YOUR PIECE FOR THE CHRISTMAS PROGRAM..

"SO THE WORDS SPOKEN THROUGH JEREMIAH THE PROPHET WERE FULFILLED: 'A VOICE WAS HEARD IN RAMA, WAILING AND LOUD LAMENTS; IT WAS RACHEL WEEPING FOR HER CHILDREN, AND REFUSING ALL CONSOLATION BECAUSE THEY WERE NO MORE.'" GOOD GRIEF!!

MEMORIZE IT, AND BE READY TO RECITE IT BY NEXT SUNDAY!

© 1970 United Feature Syndicate, Inc.

Wherever Paperbacks Are Sold

FOR THE LOVE OF PEANUTS

☐ 02710 X	For the Love Of Peanuts (2)	50p
☐ 04409 8	Who Do You Think You Are, Charlie Brown (4)	50p
☐ 04305 9	Fun With Peanuts (5)	50p
☐ 04295 8	Here Comes Snoopy (6)	50p
☐ 04318 0	You're My Hero, Charlie Brown (7)	50p
☐ 04406 3	This Is Your Life, Charlie Brown (8)	50p
☐ 04294 X	Let's Face It, Charlie Brown (9)	50p
☐ 04407 1	Slide Charlie Brown Slide (10)	50p
☐ 10788 X	Good Grief, Charlie Brown (12)	50p
☐ 10595 X	Here's To You, Charlie Brown (13)	50p
☐ 10541 0	Nobody's Perfect Charlie Brown (14)	50p
☐ 10673 5	Very Funny, Charlie Brown (15)	50p
☐ 10761 8	Hey, Peanuts (17)	50p
☐ 12614 0	You're Too Much, Charlie Brown (21)	50p
☐ 12618 3	Here Comes Charlie Brown (22)	50p
☐ 12543 8	The Wonderful World of Peanuts (24)	50p
☐ 12544 6	What Next, Charlie Brown? (26)	50p
☐ 15828 X	Have It Your Way, Charlie Brown (29)	50p
☐ 17322 X	You're Something Special, Snoopy (33)	50p
☐ 12838 0	You're a Brave Man Charlie Brown (18)	50p
☐ 12786 4	We Love you, Snoopy (19)	50p
☐ 12521 7	You've Done it Again, Charlie Brown (23)	50p

All these books are available at your local bookshop or newsagent, or can be ordered direct from the publisher. Just tick the titles you want and fill in the form below.
Prices and availability subject to change without notice.

CORONET BOOKS, P.O. Box 11, Falmouth, Cornwall.
Please send cheque or postal order, and allow the following for postage and packing:

U.K. – One book 22p plus 10p per copy for each additional book ordered, up to a maximum of 82p.

B.F.P.O. and EIRE – 22p for the first book plus 10p per copy for the next 6 books, thereafter 4p per book.

OTHER OVERSEAS CUSTOMERS – 30p for the first book and 10p per copy for each additional book.

Name ———————————————————————————

Address ————————————————————————————

————————————————————————————————